Two Worlds One Mother

Two Worlds One Mother

TWO WORLDS ONE MOTHER

Kate Baker-Loveday

Lyra's Light

Contact: Kate@lyraslight.co.uk

Two Worlds One Mother

DEDICATION

I dedicate this book to my beautiful girls; my earthly angels and my heavenly angels, and to all mothers, parents and all angels.

IN

MEMORY

OF

Violet & Daisy

IN MEMORY

OF

....

....

....

....

"It is my belief, no one person can quantify another's loss by their own measure, and nor should they. ALL pregnancy and baby loss counts."

Kate Baker-Loveday
09.03.2019 ©

(First published - 'Violet Daisy Chain – All Pregnancy and Baby Loss Counts' – Facebook page 2019)

CONTENTS

FOREWORD

I have known Kate since 2019 when she joined our Twins Trust Bereavement group. My own identical twin boys, Charlie and Joshua, died in 1999 after surviving a few weeks in NICU. I have been the bereavement group coordinator at Twins Trust since 2014. I remember Kate joining our group and sharing her experience of her twin girls Violet and Daisy. I began following her journey and her page Violet Daisy Chain - All Pregnancy and Baby Loss Counts. Kate is a very kind and supportive member of our Facebook group and gives much needed support to many of our bereaved families. It is a special connection that we all have, being 'twin' or 'triplet' parents that have suffered the death of one or more of our babies. We have many people in our group but Kate always stands out as being one of those people that can be relied upon to help others, being empathetic at all times.

When Kate told me about her book and asked me to write the foreword I was honoured and eagerly awaited to read her book. I have read it multiple times now and on each occasion I find myself noticing something new and thinking about my own experience.

I am sure that all bereaved parents and friends and families will be able to identify with this beautifully written story and the words are brought alive further by the pictures that complement each page. There will be much that resonates with those that have experienced Baby Loss - robins, bumblebees, flowers, feathers, rainbows and butterflies to name a few. For myself, my feelings during my next pregnancy with my daughter Jess, and even with my son Samuel, were definitely brought back to the surface 'worry was never far away' while still being 'consumed by grief.'

The feelings of isolation and empty arms that Kate draws upon will be familiar as well as the powerful use of the words 'together' and 'side by side, perhaps anticipating twins: 2 butterflies, 2 rainbows...and the rainbow after a loss signifying a rainbow pregnancy.

I urge you to allow yourself to reflect as you read Kate's words. I had a lot of thoughts and emotions, allowing me to draw parallels with my own story. Stars are my reminder of my boys so I was glad to see that twinkling stars occur. It is beautifully illustrated with stars being a consistent feature throughout.

One thing that I am glad of since losing our twins Charlie, Joshua, Violet and Daisy is that I now know Kate, we have not actually ever met in person, but have exchanged many emails, messages and supportive thoughts to each other and have become friends.

Sharon Darke
Bereavement Support Group Coordinator
Twins Trust

PREFACE

'Two Worlds One Mother' was created in a profound attempt at an impartial depiction of loss. Having experienced loss myself, this considerably sensitive topic is more than close to my heart.

In 2003, I was not only fortunate to become pregnant but pregnant with twins - two little girls. I suffered very early on with hyperemesis (significant sickness) and then for the duration, apart from that, everything else was apparently good, until...

The experience of losing my twin girls, Violet and Daisy, was life changing, and while absolutely the foundation for this book, is not solely about them, or me, but is about - "loss."

Through my own personal experience and the experience of others too, I have come to recognise both the importance and the need for increasing awareness surrounding the loss of pregnancy and the loss of a baby, and how crucial support is. Therefore, it is my sincerest hope this book can not only show support to those who have lost but also help to shed some light for those who have not by serving to represent a little of what can sometimes, and without choice, remain hidden and silent.

In 2019, following a sequence of events which had taken me by surprise, I found myself wanting to help others. This is when I became the author of the 'Violet Daisy Chain – All Pregnancy and Baby Loss Counts' Facebook page. It is on this page I have shared my journey of loss, continuing into the after loss. The page was created in the hope that sharing my experience of losing Violet and Daisy, and in a place where it was accessible, could maybe help others, even if only to help raise awareness by its existence. I felt extremely vulnerable sharing my first posts and very much feared being judged, but regardless of this, and the tears, felt the purpose of sharing to be far greater than just me.

It was at this time I also became a member of some of the loss support groups, including Tommy's - Baby Loss support Group, Twins Trust - Bereavement Support Group and The Miscarriage

Association, where in some of the groups I was able to share posts from my page. When reading the posts of the other members I sadly recognised the only too familiar pain and devastation - my heart just wanted to reach out. For many, their grief was so recent and raw, my grief being some years on was neither. Instantaneously there was an overpowering sense of wanting to interact and offer support to the other members. I found being part of something I had never had the opportunity to be part of at the time of losing Violet and Daisy, surprisingly healing, and with so many years passed, this was way more significant than I could have imagined.

Since establishing the Violet Daisy Chain – All Pregnancy and Baby Loss Counts page, and becoming a member of the groups, especially within the Twins Trust -Bereavement Support Group, I have learnt so much in relation to grief - my own and others. I have also learnt, even in times of deep suffering, how selfless, kind and compassionate others can be too. I am incredibly grateful to all of those who have interacted with me personally, and on my page; such interactions have not only further strengthened my views but have also been an invaluable and empowering source of inspiration.

Writing and sharing feelings so openly and with people I had never met had all been so new to me but were increasingly becoming part of my life. I became the author of a second Facebook page - 'Poetry In Essence,' and this is when I discovered writing poetry allowed me to be expressive and creative on many levels; I could see my skills and experiences fuse. As I gained confidence and then recognition, other opportunities became available. It was a real achievement to have poems I had written published beyond my pages, such as in the Twins Trust – Bereavement Support Groups newsletters, and in books with other poets from around the world. Each and every publication, big and small have all in some way been very important to me.

As an artist with a background in fine art, design and photography, I have worked in numerous roles, including for the Arts Council England and in schools. I have worked with children of various ages and additionally those with special educational needs, all of which I absolutely loved. This was right up to when the then healthy life I once knew changed dramatically, impacting my abilities in almost every capacity, and physically, I could no longer leave the house without assistance. Prior to these changes, life had always been more about visual expression rather than words, but it was at this point in 2011, that writing became my therapy, and when I actively began writing.

Ten years on, 2021, a very significant year marking the 18th anniversary of Violet and Daisy. The year I also saw myself taking the next step in my writing journey with the hope of going solo in book publishing. An exciting time with lots of ideas, and with me in the equation, 'time' was something I definitely was going to need plenty of... It was early spring, I must have had everything going around inside my head: book ideas, pages, plans, revisiting thoughts, feelings etc., when suddenly, something sparked! My mind lit up. An idea intercepting all previous ideas and plans and I knew from that moment would take priority. Through the use of poetry, my aim was to write a meaningful short story about loss. A story with feeling, to impartially and sensitively capture something of the immeasurable and the invisible, both visually and textually, and show support while simultaneously raising awareness. I was compelled and going to give nothing short of my best efforts - this was my mission.

As I began to write I soon learnt the true scale of the challenge I had set myself - this was no short story or even a short story of a thousand stories, it was so much more... A colossal amount of time has gone into the creation of this book, far more than I could have ever previously imagined, encountering many struggles along the way, including when I realised, I was, in fact trying to achieve the impossible. To even attempt to comprehend the vastness of each individual circumstance relating to loss is impossible, yet somehow, I felt I had a responsibility. I felt by not representing each circumstance in my writing I would be being dismissive, crude, and unforgivably unfair. I was overwhelmed but was not going to give up. In my determination to continue I turned to writing to help process what I was feeling. My analogy went something along the lines of ...Like attempting to write a sacred prayer, by hand, in all the languages of the world, with a crayon, and on the reverse side of a small, rare and delicate postage stamp...

Every word had to be wholly considered, every line a fragile thread to either connect to, break or begin, and each page, like a feather, catching the rise and fall of each breath...

This book is for all who can relate, all who wish to understand, and all who wish to show their support... I feel, through its words and nature-inspired images, this symbolic journey insightfully touches on what is unseen: in hope, in loss, and in grief. It has been created with love, compassion, tears, frustration and total dedication, and is with the skills I have. Loss is utterly heart-breaking and indiscriminately impacts on the lives of many. ♥

INTRODUCTION

It must have been December 1980, when at only six years of age I can recall having my first conscious thought about wanting to be a mother. I remember it was around the time John Lennon, musician and member of the 1960's English rock band, 'The Beatles,' was shot and killed. I remember this being big news on the television but not really any detail. I just remember wishing I could be the youngest mummy to have a baby, and how I would very much like the daddy to be - Paul McCartney!

At this point of writing, I am not certain if I ever shared this memory with anyone, and from my now-adult perspective cannot believe I am sharing it here! I also cannot help but smile to myself, both at the randomness and the innocence of my child self.

It is probably fair to say, that somewhere in my heart from that point onwards I had hoped to one day be a mother.

I was born as a result of an unwanted pregnancy, which is another story but I do recall even as a young child life felt pretty complicated. I guess I must have had an idea quite early on of what type of mother I hoped to be as my late teens, and my early 20's found me questioning life and my earlier hopes. I was concerned I may well not be the good mother I one day hoped to be, understanding that being a mother was way more than just becoming or just wanting to be one.

MOTHER: -

A female parent. One who loves and affectionately regards her child, who has a close attachment and an unconditional bond.

Once a mother, be her child, unborn, living or lost, she is always...a mother.

Kate Baker-Loveday
25.03.2019

(First published on numerous media sites including 'Violet Daisy Chain – All Pregnancy and Baby Loss Counts' Facebook page – For Mother's Day 2019)

The journey through the words and images in this book attempt to embody the hopes and desires of becoming a mother/parent, but also in the recognition, that initially, hope essentially, is all we ever really have, and for some, how even the hope that is realised can also so sadly be lost...

Loss, I believe, is one of the greatest devastations a human can experience. For the purpose of this book, 'loss' specifically refers to all loss associated with pregnancy, baby and infant, the types of loss where it is primarily the mother or parents impacted, the types of loss apparently no one wants to mention, well, maybe not everyone...

Personally, some of my biggest reasons for not talking about my loss were for the fear of upsetting anyone or no one wanting to listen. There was also the fear of others having expectations and opinions of how I should or should not be coping. Whether those reasons were true, perceived or in combination it was how I felt at the time. Since then, from the shared experiences of those close to me, within the loss support groups and on the Violet Daisy Chain – All Pregnancy and Baby Loss Counts Facebook page, I know I am not alone. The feelings of being isolated within families, friendships and the workspace, even in close partnerships is very much an issue. I feel this to be a tragedy within humanity. When we most need to be supported in a time of grief some of those closest to us would seem to shy away. We of course all cope with situations very differently, and for different reasons, it is sometimes just so very sad.

My hope is, that this depiction of loss can act as a small window of consideration to some of the emotions encountered, to help 'loss' and all that surrounds it to become more openly accepted, and not remain a topic for the shadows. Awareness is increasing all of the time with the continuous and the incredible hard work, support and research of the charities, not forgetting the considerable individual efforts too, but the actual 'realness' and the 'raw-ity' are somehow still only barely acknowledged in everyday life, not enough for those who need it to be more, while respecting also, that that acknowledgement, certainly is not for all.

This book has been a challenge of all challenges to write, for so many reasons. It has been written freely rather than formally due in part to the sensitive content and my style - I do have a tendency to use words which are not necessarily in the dictionary and are really more for personal emphasis/occasions when word-finding is a challenge, but in overall content, it is with the understanding and experience I have relating to 'loss' I wanted to create this book. A book that looks into the depths with the intention to connect, both emotionally and symbolically, while sensitively and compassionately portraying the equally important aspects of loss; the visible and the invisible - a book which seeks to capture a glimpse of the life in two worlds...

'Two Worlds One Mother' has been written for and in honour of every mother who has lost, and in memory and honour of all those lost - the beyond precious - 'little wings.' It is my heartfelt belief those who understand loss will relate, and sadly identify, even if only in part, but this book is also intended for all those who do not too, who maybe wish to gain a little more of an understanding, or possibly show support to someone who has lost around them. What is imperative to understand is, that this is a respectful attempt at an impartial representation of loss, and not an actual or definitive one. No two experiences of grief are the same, just as, no two worlds are the same... ♥

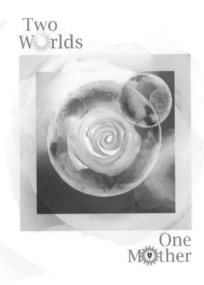

CHAPTER

• ONE •

Birds were busy collecting twigs building nests in bushes and trees

Buzzing loudly in the pussy willow dusted with pollen were bumblebees

Spring was undoubtedly in the air and the sky a beautiful shade of blue

Two courtship feeding Robins, as she looked up, swiftly flew into her view

In that very moment, she had an inkling, feeling something inside and deep within

Uncertain at first, then, with excitement her eyes wide and twinkling

Again! Baby kicked again! The thought filling her with sheer delight

Then again! Only this time in her watchfulness she had gleefully caught sight

The fusion of masculine and feminine ~ a point of conception

An act of love, maybe planned, maybe unexpected or maybe with intervention and inception

For her, discovering being pregnant was definitely unexpected and met with resounding joy

Fondly she recalled countless daydreams of one day being a mother to a baby girl or baby boy

Radiant, she was literally glowing

Bountiful, like an empress with a neatness she was duly showing

Blooming and in a pure state of serenity

She really was the epitome of a happy and healthy mother-to-be

With wonder and at any opportunity she imagined what life with her new baby would be

Especially enjoying being outside whiling away hours when the days were hot, hazy and trouble-free

She recalled a heightened sense of awareness to the roses, billowy and delicately fragrant, the magnificence of the lilies and the sunflowers being bright and bold

Filled with such expectancy and hope, what happened next was an eventuality no one could have predicted, seen or knowingly foretold

The heat this night made for a most restless night and was so terribly difficult for her to sleep

Though not, apparently for her soundly sleeping partner, who did no more than make a single twitch or peep

She considerately paced the bedroom floors, almost cringing with each yawning creak

Carefully she opened windows and doors, fridge peeking and tidy-up tweaking as around the house in her wakefulness she did sneak

With an unnerving awareness of increasing discomfort, what to do next she really did not know...

By midday and now more of an imminent concern for she had also had a show

The sight of blood made her little heart sink for she felt with dread this was not a good sign

She should rest, she attempted to reassure herself as now was not baby's due date or time!

The saddest of saddest things to happen to her unavoidably happened later that day

There was nothing anyone on earth or the angels above could do, baby's life had silently slipped away...

Birth, contradictory by all definitions, tragically took place in the early hours of morning

The harshest of realities on what would be the darkest of days where twilight remained till dusk from its dawning

Inconceivable the reality of holding lifelessness...In her aching arms, she bore the unbearable, holding with such tenderness

Tears, like giant drops of rain, fell, the pain...measureless

Again and again, sobs took her breath; her poor heart was broken, broken with disbelief

Questioning over and over in her search for clues, she was consumed, consumed by the great shadow of grief

Angry, she blamed herself, feeling so isolated since she and baby were parted

The weight of sadness moved sluggishly through her veins like liquefied lead and she was so profoundly heavy-hearted

Home with empty arms, they stood as the vision of hope and joy dissolved; surrealism hung in the air all through the house but especially in what was to be their poor baby's room

There amidst the feeling of stark emptiness was a quietness and monochromatic shadows replaced colour as if all had somehow been swallowed by gloom

****

Weeks and months passed which turned into years...

Never being with child now one of her greatest fears

****

Flowers daubed accents of colour like paint on canvas, trees were adorned with blossom and fresh green leaf and roses...they were just beginning to bud

A most beautiful and perfect day to be married, feeling content as a measure of happiness returned, she never thought could

That night, as newlyweds, under a corpulent bright moon and stars which scintillated with extra sparkle, they did celebrate

For now, she did not dare to imagine her future or what was held in the mysterious hands of fate...

Daybreak brought soft glimmering light as it shone through the trees and sounds like faint whispers which carried in the breeze

Time spent being at one with nature was a reprieve from the masked smiles, a most welcome source of comfort and ease

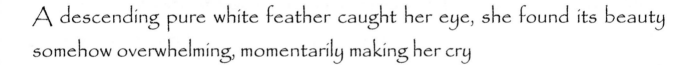

A descending pure white feather caught her eye, she found its beauty somehow overwhelming, momentarily making her cry

For she truly was the most sentient of spirits, a fact she neither would not nor could not in any way deny

Engaged in a fluttering dance two butterflies appeared, one an

orange-tip, the other, a small blue

Exhausted, bed bound with sickness, a sickness she thought would maybe last a day, or even two, but then it was the next day and the next day too!

It was then whilst she lay welcoming the butterflies' gentle distraction when a thought, she had whimsically wondered upon she pondered if it could verily be true?!

This resulted in a curiosity she simply could not quiet...One line appeared and then another...There were definitely two!

First, a feeling of uncertainty, followed by cautious but definite excitement, then, finally, an explosion of tears

The news really was the best news ever, except deeply interwoven painful memories gave rise to seemingly unsurmountable fears

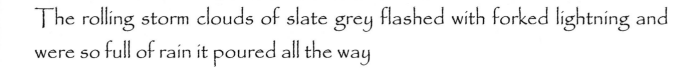

The rolling storm clouds of slate grey flashed with forked lightning and were so full of rain it poured all the way

The waiting room had a most spectacular view where in the distance she could see bright rainbows, two... Two! She thoughtfully heard herself say

A thought so right and certain in her mind she felt she actually said it out loud for all to hear

The first scan, not quite what they anticipated or had expected to find but the images were evident and clear!

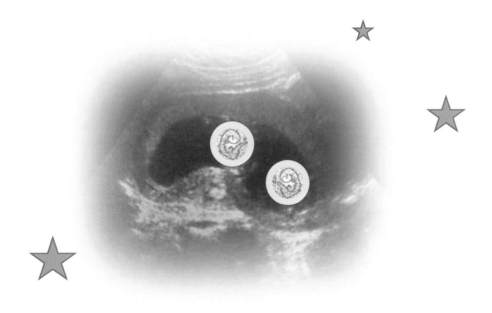

Two little tiny babies...She lingered on the thought...Two little tiny babies, their tiny, tiny hearts beating inside, two little tiny babies, together, side-by-side...

Worry was never far away but being pregnant with twins she somehow felt to be more than a miracle and her heart bounced with a happiness she simply could not hide

Then came the most terrible shock, failure screamed at her so loudly her body like an earthquake tremored and shook

The screen where she had last seen her two babies alive, she in that moment could no longer look

Words were spoken but the reality deafening, she could no longer hear what was said

Discovering one twin had somehow died was torturous; she was helpless, inconsolable and devastated, totally devastated

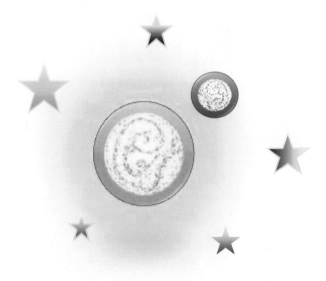

With nervous anticipation, the final months passed while contradictions of bittersweet circumstance left her emotions frayed as well as tangled from threads all unwound

The twins' arrival was early, the trees were all bare, the sun pale and snow covered the ground

This was no magical snow scene, not in their world, instead the unimaginable descended upon them like an indelible ash they could not wash away

Crushed with sorrow, the goodbye to their precious little twin who had died broke their fragile hearts in every way...

A most dramatic scene where both dark and light ends of the scale were cast at once, there were no shades of grey, only extreme contrast

Then, the moment they had longed for came at last...

A sweet embrace of purest love, they in turn held close their precious twin who survived

For her, far, far away, somewhere in the deepest depths, her soul fluttered her wings as if from the dead she herself had been revived

A new life to behold, to treasure...

She had been shrouded in a golden flecked darkness, like a midnight sky that twinkles with stars; she knew she was blessed beyond measure

Nature's nuances and ever-changing splendour inspired contemplation, peace and spiritual connection, sometimes invoking feelings where she was deeply reflective

On this occasion it was the turning autumn leaves, they appeared to blaze like tiny flames, flickering as if on fire in the setting sun, in that moment she saw how distance had given her perspective

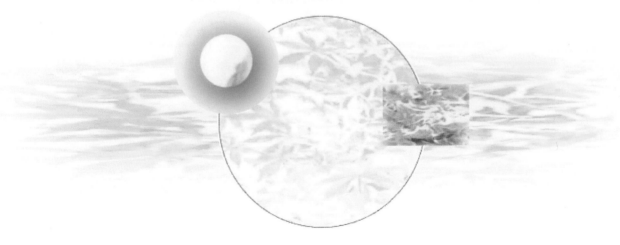

Hiding feelings to protect others and herself was no less than exhausting, she was aware her journey had not been easy but felt the importance of being able to see with clarity

With time she learnt to forgive herself, others too, recognising life cannot always be what is believed to be needed, wanted or hoped for in reality

Life taught her pain and sorrow only exist because of hope and great love, how experiences of such are often beyond control and were not only part of who she was, but were as much her destiny

She acknowledged, where possible she had always strived to give her best efforts and accepted no one and nothing could change what she knew in her heart...not in all eternity

Irreversible changes of cataclysmic significance had indeed taken place, the bottom of one world already turned on its head had subsequently fallen into an invisible other

The seen and the unseen, two equally important dimensions, two worlds where universally, unquestionably, unmistakably and undoubtedly, with engraved footprints on her heart, the resonating echoes of tiny heartbeats in her soul and angels as her witness, with all the love in her heart, ultimately, she would forever be one and the same...

A mother.

ACKNOWLEDGEMENTS

Firstly, to the wonderful and extraordinary members of my family – all of them. Thank you.

With extra special thanks to my lovely mum and dad for being such incredible humans, and for choosing me. I love you always Mum and Dad! Also, to the man who both drives me insane, and fills my heart with love – I cannot begin to imagine where on this earth I would be without him. This man is my rock of a husband, Jason. Thank you, Jason, for all you do, for being the father of our four girls, and for still being by my side through everything. Then, of course, to my now grown up beautiful girls...my heartbeats - I could not be any more proud. You both have taught, and continue to teach me so much, are my driving force, and keep me going when times are tough – thank you, Freya, and thank you, Winter. If I did not give Violet and Daisy a mention here, somehow it would not feel quite right, for they are the reason for this book, and have inadvertently been my guides - thank you to all my girls. ♥♥♥♥

Next, I would like to thank my friends for lighting up my life in some way, and for choosing to have me in their lives when there are so many amazing people to know in this world - I am both humbled and grateful. I absolutely treasure you all, and am quite certain some of you are angels too... Thank you for being part of my journey.

I would like also to individually thank those who have specifically supported me with the creation of this book: my longest-standing friend, and sister as far as we are both concerned, Tracey Staplehurst; the lovely, Rebecca Loveday, my sister-in-law; my dear friend since our university days, Colette Swires; and someone who has been right by my side since the playground conversations when dropping our girls off at school, Sue Quinn, affectionately known as, Ruby-Sue. When I finally gained the courage to ask, these fabulous individuals, each without hesitation kindly gave their precious time to read through my writing, checking for mistakes etc., all giving considerate feedback, but that's not it...

You all gave something of yourselves in your responses, each one making me feel my efforts were somehow worthy. Thank you - I cannot tell you how much this has meant...

My next thank you is to, Sharon Darke. Sharon, you are not only an inspiration through your work but your altruistic drive. You care about everyone within the Twins Trust Bereavement Support Group, and your efforts are seemingly tireless. When I contacted you to ask you if you would be interested in writing the foreword for this book your response was immediate, and with the most reassuring enthusiasm. You have been so very kind towards me, in my individual efforts, and in my efforts to show support to others too, you have undoubtedly become a valued friend... Thank you, Sharon – thank you so much.

Collectively, my thanks go to all the poets, members, admins and moderators of the various poetry groups I have been a member of, with special thanks to Marites Ritumalta, founder of Poetry Planet, for not only providing a nurturing space and helping me to become more confident as a writer but also for being the first to publish my poetry in a book; this was a huge milestone for me – thank you.

The list below are sources of support I would also very much like to give a mention to express my thanks:

- ♥ Tommy's – Baby Loss Support Group

- ♥ Miscarriage Support Group

- ♥ The Good Grief Trust

- ♥ KGH Charity Fund

- ♥ Twins Trust – Bereavement Support Group

I feel privileged all have in some way made a difference to me personally; their work and support are exceptional. In return, when possible and where appropriate I have tried to show my support in various ways including sharing and interacting with posts on social media, and via various donations.

**One group in particular, for both personal and obvious reasons, has been a very important part of this journey and is why I have chosen from any sale of this book to contribute to, the Twins Trust. The donation would equate to a percentage of the total amount paid on each book sold less the printing costs only. Initially, the idea for the amount to donate was inspired by a Twins Trust fundraising event called the 5.80 challenge, and in support of this event, I felt I would like to donate 5.80%. Since then, with consideration to several factors, and wishing the donation to be ongoing, I have decided I would no longer like to donate 5.80%, but 10%, and it is my wish for this contribution to be on any sale of this book made for the rest of my lifetime.

Finally, to all who have shown support in any capacity: to my pages, my book, my efforts, and me as a person, I simply would not have arrived at this point without you – A most gracious and heartfelt thank you to you all – Thank you. ♥

GLOSSARY

Adversity	- difficult, unfavourable, misfortunate, unpleasant
Advocate	- defends or supports a cause/interest on behalf of others
Altruistic	- Unselfish and concerned for the welfare of others
Anthology	- Collection of works – artistic, literary/poetic, or musical
Bountiful	- Abundant, plenty, fruitful
Cataclysmic	- Effects, disaster, catastrophic, tragic
Epitome	- The essence, illustrates or possesses the qualities of
Hyperemesis	- Significant sickness during pregnancy
Indelible	- Marks or memories which cannot be removed, washed or forgotten - permanent
Nuances	- subtle, small differences and distinctions
Raw-ity	- To express 'rawness' in terms of pain – variant for my personal emphasis (Not in a dictionary)
Sentient	- feeling - to feel, perceive, alive, senses, awareness
Unsurmountable	- Obstacle which cannot be overcome, overwhelmed, unbeatable, hopeless

Links to follow Kate:

Facebook: http://www.facebook.com/violetdaisychain

Facebook: http://www.facebook.com/poetryinessence

ABOUT THE AUTHOR

Kate Baker-Loveday is a U.K. born artist, author, and poet, who with deep feelings, and the love of nature as her inspiration, has created, Two Worlds One Mother.

Kate is a devoted mother and wife and lives at home with her family. She is an author on several platforms with pages on social media where she shares her journey of baby loss, and also her poetry. Kate has achieved recognition in poetic circles and has been awarded a winner and certificates of excellence, she also has poems published in several anthologies with poets from around the world.

Having attended both Art College and University, Kate has qualifications in Fine Art, Design, and Photography. She has exhibited in numerous settings and galleries where she received media interest and an interview by BBC Radio. With a diverse range of creative skills, Kate has gained experience working with children in various capacities and with individuals from all walks of life, experiences she has truly come to cherish, especially since being impacted by significant changes in her health.

Kate Baker-Loveday is without question, a sensitive individual and very much believes in the importance of acknowledging emotions. Kate loves wholeheartedly and values every one of her relationships; humans and animals alike. As a mother, she feels she has encountered some of her most significant life lessons and through her own unique experience of loss understands something of emotional adversity. In Kate's opinion grief is not a weakness or something that can be measured and she hopes through her book she can advocate this and help bring to light the true impact baby loss has.

LIST OF HELPFUL CONTACTS

Below is a list of a few contacts which I felt may be helpful for those who are looking to connect with others either in a similar situation to themselves or for seeking further advice.

If in a situation where it is felt medical help/support/attention is required please seek professional advice via your local doctor or health services.

♥ MISCARRIAGE ASSOCIATION:

TEL: 01924 200799   (Helpline)

EMAIL: info@miscarriageassociation.org.uk

♥ SANDS – (STILLBIRTH AND NEONATAL DEATH SOCIETY):

WEB: www.sands.org.uk

HELPLINE: 0808 1643332

TEL: 020 7436 7940

EMAIL: helpline@sands.org.uk

♥ TOMMY'S:

WEBSITE: www.tommys.org

TELEPHONE/GENERAL: 02073983400

SOCIAL MEDIA SITES: @tommys

HELPLINE/MIDWIVES: 0800 0147 800 (weekdays only 9am-5pm)

EMAIL: midwife@tommys.org

❤ TWINS TRUST – BEREAVEMENT SUPPORT GROUP:

WEBSITE: www.twinstrust.org/bereavement

TWINLINE: 0800 1380509   (Free helpline, weekdays 10am-1pm and 7-10pm)

TEL: 01252 332344

EMAIL: bereavementsupport@twinstrust.org

Other helpful contacts: -

❤ THE GOOD GRIEF TRUST:

WEB: www.thegoodgrieftrust.org

EMAIL: hello@thegoodgrieftrust.org

❤ NHS:

TEL: 111   (For urgent help)

TEL: 999   (In an Emergency)

❤ SAMARITANS:

TEL: 116 123   - Free (Anytime, day or night)

The Beloved Leaf ©

(Page of names contributed by the bereaved and dedicated to the dearly beloved ♥)

The Beloved Leaf © • • • Stuart Hambidge • • Bobby Charles • • Alton-Scott twin girls • • Nikita, Marie, Nicole and baby Paul • • Soren Gerald Hennebeck • • Archie & Ayla • • Eleanor Mae Wallis • • Ross Alexander • • Daithi O Hare • • Barnaby Grice • Chester Grice • • Maisie Gibbons • • Sigh Angel • • John William Michael Craig • • Fraser Anderson • • Sidney Avison • • Baby Marsh-James • Elan-Hedd • • Baby Julier • • KEA & AVA • • Bobby-Mitchell Lucy • • Jade Ann & Jazel Valenka • • Freya Mitchell • • Aiden & Olivia • • Mila-Grace & Isla-Rose • • Christian • Mateo • • Baby Osborne • • Violet & Daisy • • Lily Marie Reah • • Scarlett May & Brooke Catherine • • Charlie Bear, Frankie Bear and Little Bear • • Jax and Julian Hermanson • • Joy Naomi Owens • Elliott James Owens • • Harry and Oliver Sharpe • • Samantha Romain • • Julianna Rose and Madeline Elizabeth • • Ellie • • Enyah Begley-Johnson • • Scarlett Kathleen • • Eva & Emily Booth • • Jensen • • Jaxon Arthur Shaun Baldwin • • Antony Cowdrey • • Hugo May-Plumer • • Charlie and Joshua Darke • • Joseph James & Thomas Andrew • • Grace & Thomas Doran • • Isla Zoey Jeffries • • John-Paul and Christopher Paul Moore • • Rūtelė and Matthew Jnr. Kislick • • Arthur & Archie Carr • • Robinson twin boys • • Louis Robin Matthew Winnington • • Seren Purnell • • Jennifer Rose Turner • • Charlie Lily • Sophie Faith • • Arlo-Aaron Jon • • Molly and Maisy • Poppy • • Albie James • • • ♥♥

●

'Pam'

1947 – 1993

● ● ●

'Dee'

1957 – 2022

●

Printed in Great Britain
by Amazon